MW00635155

This Book Belongs To

_____

God's Gift of Love
A CHRISTMAS STORY

by Solveig Muus

Illustrations by Michael Adams

Text copyright (c) 2014 by Aquinas Press
Illustrations copyright (c) 2014 by Michael Adams
Book layout and design by Randy Wollenmann

ISBN 978-1-61796-100-7
Library of Congress Number 2013901161

Published by Aquinas Press, Phoenix, Arizona
Manufactured in China. All rights reserved.

Fourth Printing, July, 2018

*I*magine Bethlehem the day before Jesus was born.

The next day wouldn't be Christmas, because the beautiful baby we know as the Son of God wasn't in the manger yet. No choirs were singing "Peace on earth" or "Rejoice! Good will to all" or any other Christmas song. No Christmas trees. People were lonesome in those days. They said to one another, "I wonder if God really loves us?" They wished that God did not seem so far away.

This made God sad. It made the people sad, too, because no matter what they did, they could never be good enough for a perfect, holy and blameless God.

But all hope was not lost, because God had a plan.

Through the years, God sent prophets to tell his people about a redeemer they would one day call the Messiah. One of the greatest prophets, Isaiah, proclaimed that the Messiah would be born of a virgin, and he would be called Immanuel, which means *God with us*. The virgin was Mary, and Jesus was her child. The prophet Micah announced that the Messiah would be born in Bethlehem, which is the town where Jesus was born.

Christmas Prayer
O Lord, long ago You promised to send us a Redeemer born of a virgin. When You were ready, You sent us Your Son, Jesus, born of the Virgin Mary. Please help us prepare the way for Jesus to be born again in our hearts this Christmas. Amen.

God wanted his people to know him, and to know how much he loved them. One way he demonstrated his love was to choose certain people to work for him, and sometimes what he asked them to do was very difficult. The most special of these was Mary, a virgin who lived in a little town in Israel called Nazareth.

One day an angel named Gabriel appeared to Mary and said, "Hail Mary! You are full of grace. Do not be afraid, for the Lord is with you!" Gabriel told Mary that God wanted her to bear His Son, and to call him Jesus. Mary said, "Behold, I am the servant of the Lord. May it be done unto me as you have said."

And so it was that Mary agreed to obey God. Mary couldn't sleep that night; she was too excited. This could not have been an easy decision, but Mary was a faithful servant of God; she would do this thing that he asked. And because she said "Yes," Jesus was born, God was able to save the world, and the gates of heaven were opened.

"And coming to her, he said, 'Hail, favored one! The Lord is with you. Do not be afraid, Mary, for you have found favor with God. Behold, you will conceive and bear a son, and you shall call him Jesus.'"
Luke 1:28-30

When Mary awoke the next morning, she was happy. It seemed quite impossible, but she was a woman of deep faith, and she knew it was true.

Mary remembered that the angel told her that her cousin, Elizabeth, was expecting a child, and Mary decided to visit her. She got dressed, ate, let her family know where she was going and why, and set off on a journey to Judea where her cousin lived.

It took Mary a few days, so when she arrived at the home of Zacharias and Elizabeth, she was very weary from the long journey.

Elizabeth hurried to share the good news with Mary about what the Lord had done, but when she saw Mary and heard her voice, the baby inside her jumped with joy!

At that moment, Elizabeth was filled with the Holy Spirit and she said, "Blessed are you among women, and blessed is the baby you carry. It is such a blessing that you, the mother of my Lord, came to visit me!"

"When Elizabeth heard Mary's greeting, the infant leaped in her womb, and Elizabeth, filled with the Holy Spirit, cried out, 'Most blessed are you among women, and blessed is the fruit of your womb."
Luke 1:41-42

Not long afterwards, an angel of the Lord came to Joseph in a dream. The angel said, "I have come to tell you that Mary, your betrothed, will have a son sent by God. You will name him Jesus, and he will save his people from their sins." When he heard this, Joseph was surprised, and also a little afraid, but he was faithful to the Lord, so he married Mary and cared for her tenderly.

Not long after Joseph and Mary were married, the Roman emperor, Caesar Augustus, decreed that all people should pay taxes. But first, each person had to go to his birthplace to register, to have his name written on a list called a census.

Joseph and Mary also needed to be listed on the census. Joseph was of the family of King David, whose birthplace was Bethlehem. So from Nazareth they traveled down the mountains to the river Jordan. They followed the long river almost to its end. Then they climbed up the mountains of Judah until finally, they reached the little town of Bethlehem.

"In those days a decree went out from Emperor Augustus that all the world should be registered. All went to their own towns to be registered."

Luke 2:1, 3

The stars shone dimly that night in Bethlehem as Joseph and Mary, weary from travel, searched for a place to rest. The town bustled with visitors who had come to have their names written on the emperor's list. No one knew that Mary was about to become the mother of the Son of God. Everywhere they went, people said, "There is no room for you."

Mary paused to feel the cool wind on her face and the ache in her weary bones. She knew that her time had come. She would give birth that very night.

Joseph tried again to find a place for Mary to rest. He approached a small inn and knocked at the door. When a man answered the door, Joseph asked, "Do you have a room where we can sleep tonight? My wife is with child; she will have the baby at any moment."

"I'm truly sorry," the innkeeper said. "My inn is full. There is no room for you here."

"Joseph also went from the town of Nazareth in Galilee to Judea, to the city of David called Bethlehem, because he was descended from the house and family of David. He went to be registered with Mary, to whom he was engaged and who was expecting a child."
Luke 2:4-5

hen the innkeeper looked at Mary's face. He felt compassion for this woman; he could see how much she needed a place to rest. "You can sleep in the stable with the animals," he said. "It's the best I can do for you."

They went to the stable where Mary could rest, surrounded by the comforting sounds of the farm animals. Joseph made a bed for her out of the softest hay he could find.

There, in the stable in Bethlehem, Mary gave birth to the baby Jesus, and she was filled with joy. She wrapped him in swaddling cloths to keep him warm. Somewhere in the back of the stable Joseph found a manger that was used to feed the cows and the oxen. He emptied it, carefully cleaned it, and used it to make a tiny bed for the baby. Mary laid her newborn son in the manger and watched over him as he slept.

"And she gave birth to her firstborn son and wrapped him in bands of cloth, and laid him in a manger, because there was no place for them at the inn."
Luke 2:7

That night, under the same starry sky, some shepherds tended their flocks of sheep in a nearby field. Some watched the sheep, tending to their comfort, while others gathered to share stories, and to rest.

Suddenly the night sky exploded with light, frightening the poor shepherds. Out of the light, an angel of the Lord appeared to them and said,

"Do not be afraid, for I bring you good tidings of great joy for all people. This day in Bethlehem a Savior is born who is Christ the Lord. You will find him wrapped in swaddling cloths, lying in a manger."

A great gathering of angels joined the first angel. Together they sang their praises to God. "Glory to God in the highest," they sang. "And on earth, peace, good will toward all people."

Still shocked and dazed, the shepherds looked at each other in awe. Was it true that the Savior had come at last and so near to their own humble homes? "Let us hurry," the shepherds said to one another. "Let us go now to Bethlehem. We must see this child!"

"Then an angel of the Lord stood before them, and the glory of the Lord shone around them, and they were terrified. But the angel said to them, 'Do not be afraid; for see – I am bringing you good news of great joy for all the people: to you is born this day in the city of David a Savior, who is the Messiah. '"

Luke 2:8-11

When they entered the town of Bethlehem, the shepherds looked for stables where there would be a manger, as the angel said. It did not take long, as there was a very bright star that appeared in the sky that night, showing them the way.

The shepherds found Joseph and Mary in the stable watching over the baby asleep in the manger. They looked at the child, and they were filled with awe and wonder once again. "You would not believe it!" they exclaimed to a puzzled Mary and Joseph. "We were in the field, and an angel came and told us the news."

The next day, the shepherds told the people in the village all the things the angel had said. Their story amazed everyone who heard it. The word spread; there was excitement in the air. Most had seen the star that night, and wondered what it meant. Mary smiled at these things with wonder and kept them quietly in her heart.

Having seen the child, the shepherds returned to their field praising God for all they had seen and heard.

"The shepherds said to one another, 'Let us go now to Bethlehem and see this thing that has taken place, which the Lord has made known to us.' So they went in haste and found Mary and Joseph, and the child lying in the manger."
Luke 2:15-16

There was among the enthralled shepherds a young boy who heard of the miracle birth and wanted to see for himself the child named Jesus. He was very excited, but also sad because he had no gift to bring for the newborn babe. All he had in the world to call his own was his drum.

Knowing of his sadness, God visited him that night in a dream, telling the shepherd boy that he did, indeed, have a gift to give. God said his gift would be his drum, and that playing it for the child would make him very happy. God told the boy that, like the ancients who sent news of important events to neighboring villages using their drums, his drum-beats, too, would be heard in the wind, and the good news of the miracle birth would spread near and far.

When the shepherd boy awoke, he was filled with joy, knowing that he had something to offer the child Jesus. So he gathered his sheep, picked up his drum, and set off to find the baby and share the good news of his birth with the world.

"And when they had seen, they made known abroad the saying which was told them concerning this child."
Luke 2:17

It was a rule among the Jews that the first boy born to a family was to be taken to the Temple to present him to the Lord. When Jesus was barely a month old, Joseph and Mary brought him there.

Living in the nearby town of Jerusalem at that time was a very old holy man named Simeon. The Lord had told him that he would not die until he had seen the Christ, or Savior, whose coming had been predicted in the Bible.

One day the Spirit of the Lord urged Simeon to go to the Temple. He went, and was there when Joseph and Mary came with the baby Jesus. When Simeon saw the child, the Lord let him know that this was the Christ who had been promised. Simeon took Jesus in his arms and gave thanks:

"Lord, now let thy servant depart in peace, according to thy word: For mine eyes have seen thy salvation, which thou hast prepared before the face of all people; a light to lighten the Gentiles, and the glory of thy people Israel."

Then Simeon blessed Joseph and Mary. He also told Mary some of the things the future would hold for her and for her son.

"And Simeon blessed them and said to Mary his mother, 'Behold, this child is appointed for the fall and rising of many in Israel, and for a sign that is opposed... so that thoughts from many hearts may be revealed.'"
Luke 2:34-35

A few days after Jesus was born, wise men called Magi also came to visit him. They had traveled a long way on camels and horses to the land of Judea.

Bethlehem was in Judea, but at first the Magi didn't know to look there. They asked everyone, "Where is he who has been born King of the Jews? For we have seen his star in the East and have come to worship him." But no one seemed to know.

King Herod, the old ruler of Judea under Caesar, was jealous and afraid. He thought, "People are asking about a new king? How can this be? I am the ruler here." He demanded that the chief priests of the people tell him where to find this baby. "In Bethlehem," they told him.

So King Herod sent the Magi to Bethlehem to search for the baby. "If you find him," King Herod said, "let me know, so I can go and worship him too." But secretly, old King Herod had an evil plan to kill the baby.

"Wise men from the East came to Jerusalem, asking, 'Where is the child who has been born king of the Jews? For we observed his star at its rising, and have come to pay him homage.'"

Matthew 2:1-2

The Magi continued on their journey. Each night, they looked up to find the same bright star they had followed before. They happily followed it again, this time all the way to Bethlehem. There the star came to shine over the baby Jesus.

The Magi saw the baby with his mother, Mary, and knew at once that he was the king. They rejoiced, they praised God, and worshipped the baby as the Lord, the Messiah. Then they opened their treasures and gave him gifts of gold, frankincense, and myrrh – gifts worthy of a king, as was their custom.

Though it was a joyfilled day indeed, that night, God warned the Magi in a dream not to go back and tell King Herod about the baby Jesus. So they returned home a different way.

"On entering the house, they saw the child with Mary his mother; and they knelt down and paid him homage. Then, opening their treasure chests, they offered him gifts of gold, frankincense and myrrh."

Matthew 2:11

God also sent a warning to Joseph. An angel of the Lord appeared to him and said, "Your family is in danger. Take your wife and young child and flee to Egypt, and stay there until I tell you to come back. Herod is going to search for the child to destroy him."

Because of his strong faith, Joseph knew that the angel came from God, and he trusted what the angel said. So late that night, Joseph took his wife and Jesus and the donkey, and they made the long journey to Egypt.

After some time, the angel Gabriel appeared to Joseph and said, "King Herod has died, and there is no more danger. You can return home to Nazareth now." Much relieved, Joseph, Mary and Jesus packed their few belongings and headed for home.

"Joseph rose and took the child and his mother by night and departed for Egypt. He stayed there until the death of Herod, that what the Lord had said through the prophet might be fulfilled, 'Out of Egypt have I called my son.'"
Matthew 2:14-15

When Mary, Joseph and their child finally reached Nazareth, their family and friends ran out to welcome them. They were so happy to be together again! When Joseph and Mary had left, they were a young couple, and Jesus was not even born yet; when they returned, they had a growing, four-year-old boy.

In Nazareth, they were a happy family. Joseph, a carpenter by trade, taught Jesus the fine points of his craft, and Jesus learned quickly. They laughed, they sang, they prayed together, and the Holy Spirit was with them. Mary said tenderly to her son, "Jesus, you have filled us with joy, and you have shown us all how much God loves us."

"And he went and lived in a town called Nazareth. So was fulfilled what was said through the prophets: 'He will be called a Nazarene.'"
Matthew 2:23

A Christmas Blessing

Loving God, Help us remember the birth of Jesus,

that we may share in the song of the angels,

the gladness of the shepherds,

and the worship of the wise men.

Close the door of hate

and open the door of love all over the world.

Let kindness come with every gift

and good desires with every greeting.

Deliver us from evil by the blessing which Christ brings,

and teach us to be merry with clean hearts.

May the Christmas morning make us happy to be thy children,

and Christmas evening bring us to our beds with grateful thoughts,

forgiving and forgiven, for Jesus' sake.

Amen.

--attributed to Robert Louis Stevenson